THE MAESTRO

The Maestro

by

GERARD HOFFNUNG

London
DENNIS DOBSON

First Published September 1953
Second Impression December 1953
Third impression March 1954
Fourth Impression December 1954
Fifth Impression October 1955
Sixth Impression December 1956
Seventh Impression October 1957
Eighth Impression December 1958
Ninth Impression September 1960
Tenth Impression November 1963
Eleventh Impression January 1968
Twelfth Impression December 1972
Thirteenth Impression October 1975

Printed in Belgium by
Henri Proost & Co p.v.b.a.

Published by Dobson Books Ltd
80 Kensington Church Street, London W.8

ISBN   0 234 77315 4

To
Annetta, my wife

Alerto

Introduzione

Interruzione

Preciso

Rallentando

Dolce

Affettuoso

Con amore

Con anima

Amoroso

Risoluto

Lusingando

Con delicatezza

Pizzicato

Scherzando

Giocoso

Scherzo

Giojoso

Allegro giocoso

Non troppo

Sotto voce

Piano

Pianissimo

Diminuendo

Molto diminuendo

Tacet

Pomposo

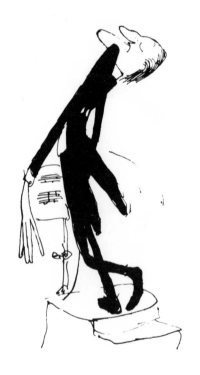

Molto pomposo

Subito piano

A cappella

A cappella continuoso

Martellato

Tempo primo

Serioso

Mesto

Doloroso

Molto doloroso

Troppo doloroso

G.P.

Affrettando

Appassionato

Basso

Vigoroso

Con forza

Molto vigoroso

Attacca

Furioso

Rinforzando

Strepitoso

Fortissimo vivacissimo

Finale furioso

Bravo bravissimo